HAVE YOU SEEN MY COIN?

BOB HARTMAN

ILLUSTRATIONS BY
ROSIE MORGAN

CWR

Published 2015 by CWR, Waverley Abbey House, Waverley Lane, Farnham, Surrey GU9 8EP, UK.
CWR is a Registered Charity – Number 294387 and a Limited Company registered in England – Registration Number 1990308.

Visit www.cwr.org.uk/distributors for a list of National Distributors.
Concept development, editing, design and production by CWR.
Illustrations by Rosie Morgan, visit rosiemorganart.com
Printed in the UK by Linney Group
ISBN: 978-1-78259-451-2

This Bible story is
found in Luke 15:8–10

Hello, there!

Look, I've got ten coins.

They're very special to me.
You can count them,
if you like.

What's that?
There are only nine?

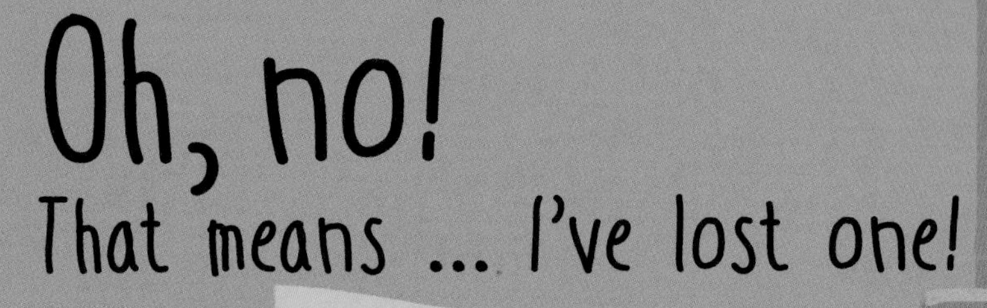

Oh, no!
That means ... I've lost one!

Do you think you could help me find it? I'll look all around my house. But I've been to lots of other places recently. Maybe you could look there ...

I was down by
the river. Perhaps
I lost it there.

CAN YOU FIND ANYTHING THAT'S ROUND?

You can, you say?
But it's not my coin.
Oh well.

I was in the vineyard, too.
It could be there, I guess.

You've spotted something?
But it's not my coin either.

The market! I was in the market doing my shopping. I might have dropped it there.

You can!

But it's not a coin.
Ah, okay.

Tell you what. I was also at the farm.

Could be there, I suppose.

You say you found something.
Something that's *not* a coin.
I see.

I did go walking up in the hills. It's a stretch, but my coin could be there.

Yes? Fantastic!
But it's not my coin.
Oh dear.

The boatyard! I was down there the other day, when the fishermen came in.

What's that? You see something?

Not my coin, though?

This is so frustrating!

How about the woods?
It's worth a try.

DO YOU SEE ANYTHING THAT HAS A PATTERN CARVED ON IT?
Yes!
But not a coin.
Sigh!

It could be outside my house, I guess.

You say you found something? And it's ... not ... a coin.

Well, thanks for looking.

I really appreciate it.

But I think my coin may be lost for good.
Time for bed now. Under the covers.
Head on the pillow ...

I don't believe it!

There's my coin!

It was in the house
all along!

I've found it! I've finally found it!

And I'm way too excited
to sleep now.

So I'm having a party!
I've invited all
my friends.
1

You can come, too, of course ... for being such a big help.
My coin was lost. And now it's found. Hooray!

LOST AND FOUND

Did you know that Jesus told this story about a lost coin in the Bible? (You can find it in Luke 15:8–10.) And this story has something very important to teach us, because it's actually all about God and us. You see:

The woman = God.

The coin = you and me.

Jesus wants us to understand that, without God in our lives, we are **lost**. But that's only the beginning of the story!

Just like the woman cared about her coin, God cares deeply about you and me. He searches and searches for us in the hope that we may come to know Him and believe in Him.

Just like the woman found her coin, we can be found.

Just like the woman threw a big party to celebrate, God throws a huge party in heaven every time someone comes to know Him as their Friend and Father.

If you want to know God as your Friend and Father, you can pray this prayer:

> ***Dear God, I want to know You as my Father in heaven. I want to welcome You into my heart and follow Your way for the rest of my life. Amen.***

If you've prayed this prayer, and really meant it in your heart, then heaven is celebrating right now! For you were once lost but now you are **found**!

BONUS ROUND!

The next time you read this book, can you also find all of these items hidden in the pages?

LOOK OUT FOR THE OTHER BOOKS IN THE LOST SERIES ...

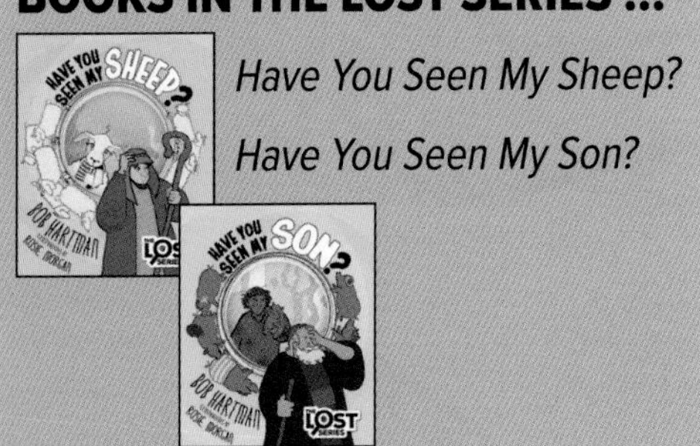

Have You Seen My Sheep?

Have You Seen My Son?

AND THE TALKING TALES ...

YUMMM!! *Elijah, the boy and the amazing famine feast*

SHHHH!! *Miriam, the baby and the secret basket boat*

PHEWW!! *Elisha, the brothers and fantastically full jars*

ZZZZZ!! *Samuel, the night and the curious calling voice*

WOWWW!! *Jairus, the daughter and the wonderful waking up*

AWWWW!! *Jesus, the grumblers and the best big hug*